THE LION STORY BIBLE
Part 1

THE LION
Story Bible

PART

1

Twenty stories from the Old Testament

Retold by Penny Frank

Illustrated by Tony Morris

LION
Children's Books

Published by
Lion Publishing plc
Sandy Lane West, Oxford, England
www.lion-publishing.co.uk
ISBN 0 7459 2034 9

This edition first published 1992
10 9 8 7 6 5 4 3

A catalogue record for this book is available
from the British Library

Printed and bound in Malaysia

CONTENTS

BEFORE YOU BEGIN...

The stories in this book all come from one much bigger book, the Bible—from the first part, called the 'Old Testament'. The introduction to each story tells you just where to find them.

The Old Testament tells the story of a people God chose for a special purpose—and of God's love and care for them through good times and bad. The story goes back almost 2,000 years. But the Bible's story begins long, long before that: it tells of the time when the world began...

In the beginning

The very first story in the Bible tells us that God made the world and everything in it.

You can find the story in the book called Genesis—the very first book in the Bible—chapter 1.

At the beginning of all time God made our world.

At first it was dark and empty. But God knew his power would change it into a beautiful place.

God made light, so there was darkness and light.

'That's good,' said God.

There was water everywhere.
God decided to keep some water in
the clouds and some on the earth.

So God made the sky for the clouds.
He kept some of the water stored in
them for when he needed rain.

'That's good,' said God.

11

God moved the water into special places on the earth and called them seas.

The water looked beautiful. The light shone on it. The edges of the water curled over onto the land in white waves.

In some places it roared around rocks and threw sparkling spray up into the air.

'That's good,' said God. 'Now we have sea and land.'

God covered the dry land with plants. Little green shoots grew to tall golden grain for the harvest.

There were trees with pink and white
blossom.

'That's good,' said God. 'There will
soon be ripe fruit to eat and nuts to
enjoy.'

There were shiny leaves of vines
climbing around the trees. God could
smell the scent of the flowers he had
made.

'What a beautiful earth it will be,'
he said.

He felt the rough bark on the huge oak trees. He saw the ferns uncurling their leaves from the damp earth.

'That's good,' said God.

God knew the plants needed warm light. He made the sun to shine in the daytime.

'That will keep my plants strong and green,' he said.

God knew he was going to make some
animals who would be awake at night.
They would need a light too, but not
such a bright, hot one as the sun.

So God made the moon and stars.

'That's good,' said God.

God watched the waves of the sea splashing on the sand. He saw the sun shining on the water. The air smelled of plants and flowers.

'These are good places to live,' he said.
'I will make fish to enjoy the water, and
I will make birds with soft feathers to
fly in the air.

'That's good,' said God. 'Now we
have fish in the sea and birds in the
air.'

'Now I shall make some tiny creatures, like this ant and this buzzing bee,' said God.

'I shall make some huge animals, like this elephant and that rhinoceros.

'Some animals will move slowly like this sloth. Some will be very fast like that cheetah. There will be animals of every size and shape.

'That's good,' said God.

God made some of the animals with soft fur and some with hard shells.

The monkeys had strong tails to help them climb, and the owls had big eyes to see in the dark.

Every animal in the sea, the air and on land was perfect.

God looked at them all and smiled. 'That's good,' said God.

Now the earth was ready for people to enjoy.

'I will make people to live here,' said God. So he made a man and a woman.

'That's good,' said God.

'They will have children,' God said.
'Then there will be plenty of people to
take care of my new land.'

God called the man Adam and the
woman Eve. They were his special
friends.

God showed the man and the woman
all the things he had made for them to
enjoy.

'Thank you,' they said. 'This earth is
a beautiful place.'

God looked at the earth. 'Yes, it is a beautiful place,' he said. 'It is very good. Now I can rest and enjoy it.'

So God rested after all his work, and enjoyed everything he had made.

Adam and Eve

When God made the world and all the
creatures on earth, everything was good. He
made people—man and woman—to be his
friends.

This story tells what happened when Adam
and Eve disobeyed God. You can find the
story in chapter 3 of Genesis.

In the very first days, when the earth
was young, God walked in his beautiful
garden.

He loved to see all the animals he had
made. Most of all he loved to come and
visit the man and woman he had made.
They were his friends. Their names were
Adam and Eve.

God usually came to see them in the evening before it was dark, when the air was cool.

They told him what they had been doing in the day.

Adam and Eve enjoyed the garden God
had made. They looked after the plants.
They picked the fruit and berries
when they were ripe.

God had said that the earth was for them to enjoy. They had chosen the names for the animals. They played with them. They splashed in the river. They watched the clouds.

'You may eat the fruit of all the trees
in the garden,' God said, 'except that
one tree in the middle.'

It was easy to obey, because there
were plenty of other good things to eat.

All the animals loved Adam and Eve.
They were not afraid of each other.

But there was one who was different.
He was a cunning snake. He was not
happy when he saw that the man and
woman were friends with God.

One day, when Eve was in the garden, the cunning snake said, 'Why don't you taste the fruit from the tree in the middle of the garden? Didn't God say you could have anything you wanted to eat?'

'We can eat anything from any of these
beautiful trees and plants,' said Eve,
'but we must never eat the fruit of
that tree, or we will die.'

'How silly you are to believe that!' hissed the cunning snake. 'You won't die! If you eat that fruit you will know as much as God. Try it, and see that I am right.'

Eve slowly turned and went to the tree.
She put her arms around it and looked
up into the leaves.

The fruit was red and shiny. In the
light of the sun it was beautiful.
It hung down quite low. She could
just reach it.

Eve took the fruit and bit it. 'It is
really delicious,' she said.

The cunning snake crept under a bush
and watched her.

Soon Adam came to look for her. He found her under the tree, eating the fruit.

'This is better than all the other fruit,' she said. 'You taste it.'

She held the fruit out and the man bit it.

Then the cunning snake smiled. But
Adam and Eve felt suddenly afraid.

They made clothes out of leaves to
cover themselves.

'Oh dear,' they said. 'When God comes
to visit us he will know we have
disobeyed him. We must hide quickly.'

They had never hidden from God
before, because they were his friends.

When God came in the evening, he called out, 'Where are you? Why are you afraid? Have you eaten the fruit of the tree in the middle of the garden?'

Adam and Eve came slowly out from
their hiding-place.

'Why did you eat that fruit?' said
God.

Adam pointed at Eve.

'She made me,' he said.

God said to Eve, 'Why did you eat the fruit?'

Eve pointed at the cunning snake.

'He made me,' she said.

God said to Adam and Eve. 'You have spoiled all my plans for you, because you have disobeyed me. Now you must go from my garden for ever. From now on you will have to work hard. You will feel pain. I will never be able to meet you here again. And when you grow old, you will die.'

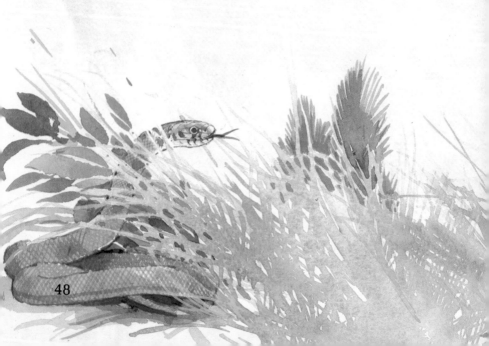

So Adam and Eve were sent away from the garden. God was sad that he could not trust them.

The man and the woman were sad that they had disobeyed God.

It was hard work to grow their own food.
They were sad that the animals did not
trust them any more.

But most of all they missed having
God as their friend.

Noah and the great flood

When God made the world, everything was good. He made the earth and the animals and the people. But the people disobeyed him and the world was spoiled.

Time passed, and things became so bad that God began to be sorry he had ever made people. But there was one person he was pleased with. His name was Noah. You can find the story in Genesis. It begins in chapter 6.

When God first made the world, everything was good. But soon God was sad when he saw the people he had put in his beautiful world. They were not the way he had made them. They were unkind. They hurt one another. They did not even try to obey God any more.

God was sad — and he was angry.

'The people who have disobeyed me must be punished,' God said. 'I shall send a great flood to wash the earth clean. My world will be as it was when I first made it. I shall begin all over again.'

There was just one man on earth who was God's friend. He was a good man, and God was pleased with him. His name was Noah.

God told Noah what he was going to do. But he promised that Noah and his family would be safe.

'I have an important job for you to do,
God told Noah. 'You will need to build
an enormous boat. You will be safe
inside while I wash the earth clean.'

God told Noah exactly how to build the special boat.

It had many rooms, a roof, a window, and a door in the side. God told Noah to make it from strong wood and to paint it with tar to keep out all the water.

Noah worked hard. He had never made a boat before but God told him just what to do.

When it was finished Noah took his whole family inside. They made sure they had all the food they needed.

God said to Noah, 'You must take into the boat a pair of all the birds and animals I have made. You must look after them while the earth is made clean, so make sure you have the food each animal likes.'

Noah and his family made the animals comfortable in the rooms of the boat. They stored away the food they needed.

When everything in the boat was as God wanted it, God shut the door of the boat.

The people who had disobeyed him were left outside.

Then God sent the rain.

The rain came in a storm. It made a terrible noise on the roof of the boat. And it went on and on.

Slowly the water rose. The boat began to float on the water.

It rained for a long time.

The animals wanted to get out and run on the grass.

Noah's family wanted to live in a house again.

But Noah said, 'You must wait.'

After many days the rain stopped. The water was so deep it covered even the mountain-tops.

Then the wind began to blow and the boat drifted on the water.

The wind blew — and the water began
to go down.

One day Noah's family could see the
mountain-tops poking up out of the
water.

Noah said, 'The birds need to stretch their wings. I will send out a raven.'

The raven flew off and did not come back. Then Noah sent out a dove, but the dove came back quickly. She could not find a dry place to rest.

The next time Noah sent out the dove
she found a tree peeping up through the
water. She broke off a twig with green
leaves and took it back to the boat.

One day the boat bumped onto some dry ground. The great flood was over.

Noah said, 'God has kept his promise. The earth will soon be dry enough for us to live on. I will send out the dove again. Perhaps she will find a place to live.'

When the dove did not come back, Noah knew that the water had gone and the earth was dry.

God said to Noah, 'My world is ready for you again. Bring out your family and all the animals.'

Noah and his family enjoyed being in the fresh air.

They stood together to say thank you to God for keeping them safe in the flood. They thanked God for his beautiful world.

'I am sad that I had to flood my earth and wash away the people and good things I had made,' said God. 'I want you to live happy lives in my world. Look!'

They looked up and saw a beautiful
shining rainbow.

'Whenever you see a rainbow,' said
God, 'remember that I have promised
never again to send a flood like this one.
You know that I always keep my
promises.'

Abraham, friend of God

God is just and good: he cannot ignore evil.
The flood was sent to wash the earth clean.
But God is also patient and loving. He kept
his promise to Noah, even though people
soon began to do wrong things again.

This story tells how God chose one man—
Abraham—and his family for a very special
purpose. You can find it in Genesis,
beginning at chapter 12.

Abraham and his wife Sarah lived in the town of Ur, in the land of Babylon. One day God told him to leave his home to go to a new land – a land which God would give to Abraham and his family.

Abraham and Sarah had no children, but God said, 'I will give this new land to you and your children, and their children after them. You will be my people.'

Abraham was getting old, but he believed God's promise that he and Sarah would one day have a child.

So they got ready for the journey.
They packed their clothes and food.
They said 'Goodbye' to all their friends.
And they set off.

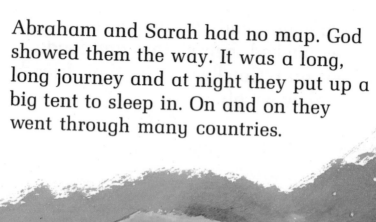

Abraham and Sarah had no map. God showed them the way. It was a long, long journey and at night they put up a big tent to sleep in. On and on they went through many countries.

Abraham and Sarah were both old, but still they had no children. God said to them, 'Look at the grains of dust on the path. Look at the stars above your tent at night. One day your family will be as many as that – too many to count.' And still Abraham trusted God.

They were glad when they came to the
new land. It had been such a long
journey. There was no house to live in,
so they lived in their big tent.

One day Abraham saw some men
going by. 'Please come in and sit down,'
he said. 'We will get you something to
eat.'

'That would be good,' said the men, 'because we have an important message for you. Your wife Sarah is going to have a baby boy.'

Sarah heard what they said and laughed. 'It is too late,' she said. 'We are too old now.'

God was sorry that Sarah did not
believe the men he had sent. But soon
Sarah knew that the message was true.
She was going to have a baby.

'Perhaps nothing is too hard for God,'
she said.

When the baby boy was born, Abraham and Sarah were very happy. They called him Isaac. God had kept his promise.

Abraham and Sarah loved their little son. They watched him play outside the tent.

The years passed. Isaac grew up tall and strong. His parents were very proud of him. They thanked God for keeping his promise.

God had given Abraham a new land and he had given him a son. How Abraham loved Isaac.

God loved Abraham. But he wanted to make sure that Abraham trusted him just as much as when he had first come to the new land.

So God said to Abraham, 'Take this son you love so much and go to the mountains you can see. I want you to offer him to me as a sacrifice.'

Poor Abraham! He wished there was
some other way to show God his love.
But he obeyed God. He took Isaac to the
mountains with some firewood and a
knife.

Isaac looked at the heap of stones on the mountain. He saw the knife and the wood.

'What shall we offer to God on the stones to show that we love him?' he asked.

Abraham was very sad but he told
Isaac that they must trust God to give
them something to put on the stones.

God did not want Isaac to die. He did not want Abraham and Sarah to be unhappy. He just wanted to be sure that Abraham would still trust and obey him.

Abraham put Isaac on top of the stones.
He picked up the knife to kill Isaac.
   Then God called, 'Abraham, stop!
Look, I have given you the animal in
that bush behind you.'

God knew now that Abraham really did trust him. He would obey whatever the cost. Abraham and Isaac were so happy. They thanked God as they made the sacrifice.

They talked about what had happened as they went down the mountain. They were so glad that they could trust God.

And as God had promised, through Isaac and his children Abraham's family did become a great nation.

Jacob and Esau

God kept his promise to make Abraham
the founder of a great nation. His son Isaac
grew up and married. Isaac and Rebecca
had twin sons—Jacob and Esau. But it was a
long time before the boys were born. Isaac
and Rebecca had grown old by the time of
this next story. You will find it in Genesis,
chapters 27 to 33.

Isaac lived in the land of Canaan.

He was old and blind. His wife
Rebecca looked after him.

Their sons were twins called Esau
and Jacob. They loved them both very
much.

When they were little boys, Esau and Jacob enjoyed playing together.

There was always plenty to do around the tent where they lived. There were hills to climb and donkeys to ride.

But as they grew older they started to enjoy different things.

'Let's go out hunting for meat,' Esau would say.

But Jacob would answer, 'No thanks. I'd rather stay at home.'

Rebecca loved Jacob best. She was glad
that he stayed at home. They talked
together as they worked.

Jacob knew that even though they
were twins, Isaac would give Esau all
the special blessings of God kept for the
first son, because he was born first.

'It's just not fair,' Jacob would say to
his mother.

Isaac was glad that Esau loved hunting.
He enjoyed eating the meat Esau
caught, while he listened to his stories.
He loved to hear about the hills and the
fields and the world he could not see.

One day when Esau was out hunting, Rebecca called to Jacob.

'Quickly, go and put on some of Esau's clothes. We will make your father give you the special blessing before Esau comes back.'

Rebecca tied goatskins around Jacob's arms, to make them feel hairy, like Esau's. Then Jacob took some food to his father.

Isaac was blind, so he put out his hand to touch his son.

'Is that you, Esau?' he asked.

'Yes, father,' said Jacob, making his voice like Esau's.

So Isaac gave Jacob the special blessing of God, kept for the first son.

Jacob and Rebecca were glad. They knew now that Jacob would be a rich man. Isaac's blessing promised him a long life and success.

Then Esau came in from hunting. He
cooked the meat and took it in to his
father.

Esau asked his father for the special
blessing. Then Isaac knew he had been
tricked.

'You are too late, my dear son,' he told
Esau.

Esau was furious when he heard what
had happened.

'My brother is a cheat. *I* should have
God's special blessing. Please give it to
me,' he begged.

'I can't,' said Isaac sadly. 'I gave it to
Jacob and I cannot take it back.'

'I will kill him,' said Esau.

Rebecca heard what Esau said. So she sent Jacob away.

'Go and stay in the land where my brother lives,' she said. 'I will send you a message when it is safe for you to come home.'

So Jacob began his journey to Haran. It was a very long way.

When night-time came, he was tired. He found a dry place on the ground and used a big smooth stone as a pillow.

As he slept, he had a dream.

He dreamed of angels on a stairway going up to the sky.

He heard a voice say, 'I am the God of Abraham and Isaac. I will be with you on your journey, and bring you safely home.'

Jacob knew that God hated his cheating, and he was very afraid. But God had said he would keep the promise he had made to Abraham for his whole family.

In Haran Jacob found his uncle, Laban. He worked hard for him for many years, though Laban was a bigger cheat than Jacob!

Jacob became a rich man with sheep
and goats of his own. He wanted to
marry Laban's beautiful daughter,
Rachel. But Laban tricked him into
marrying her older sister.

Brother Esau stayed in Canaan. He felt cheated and sad. His mother, Rebecca, died. But Esau worked hard.

He had a family and they lived in a big tent.

He often thought, 'I wish I knew where Jacob was. I would like to see him again.'

One day God told Jacob to travel back to
Canaan, the land God had promised to
Jacob's grandfather, Abraham.

Jacob took his family and animals
with him.

Jacob was afraid of meeting Esau.

'I do not deserve the care and love you have shown me all these years,' he said to God. 'But please take care of me now, as I meet Esau.'

Jacob sent presents of sheep and goats
ahead of him, in case his brother was
still angry.

But Esau ran to meet Jacob. He threw
his arms around him and kissed him —
he was so glad Jacob had come back.

God had helped Esau to forgive Jacob.
He had kept his promise to bring Jacob
home, safe and sound. The two brothers
were friends again.

Joseph
the dreamer

This story is about one of Jacob's sons—the youngest but one. It comes from Genesis, chapter 37. Joseph is one of the great heroes of the Bible, though when the story begins he is just a spoiled boy.

There was an old man called Jacob
living in Canaan. His wife had died,
but he was never lonely because he had
twelve sons.

Jacob loved all his sons, but one
was special. His name was Joseph.
And Jacob loved him best of all.

The other brothers were jealous
because Jacob made a big fuss over
Joseph. He even gave Joseph a special
coat to wear.

Joseph was not very nice. For one thing, he always ran and told his father about what his brothers were doing.

One night Joseph dreamed that all his
family were sheaves of wheat in a field.

His sheaf stood up straight and tall.
All the other sheaves bowed down to
his sheaf.

When Joseph told his brothers about the dream, they were really angry.

'Do you think we will bow down to you?' they said. 'You must be joking!'

Another time, Joseph dreamed he was
looking up into the sky. His family
were the sun, the moon and the stars.
They all bowed down to him.

Even his father was upset when he
heard about that dream.

'What kind of dream is that?' he said.
'Be quiet!'

His brothers hated him still more.

Jacob was a rich man. He had huge flocks of sheep and goats.

The animals needed grass to eat and water to drink. Often they had to be taken a long way away to find the grass and water.

Jacob's sons went with the animals to take care of them. Sometimes they walked many days just looking for grass.

Joseph stayed at home.

One day Jacob's sons had been away
with the sheep for a long time. Jacob
said to Joseph, 'I want you to go and
find your brothers. Take them some
food and see if they are well.'

Joseph walked and walked. His brothers saw him coming. They laughed behind their hands.

'Here comes the Great Dreamer,' they said.

One of them said, 'I've had enough of
his dreams. He's only come now so that
he can go back and tell our father about
us. Let's kill him.'

Another one said, 'Why don't we just throw him in that well over there?'

They all thought that was the best idea. They took off Joseph's special coat and threw him into the dried-up well.

Then they sat down to enjoy the food Joseph had brought them.

Suddenly they saw a long line of camels walking slowly over the hills. They knew the men with the camels were going to Egypt to sell their goods.

'I know,' one brother said. 'Let's sell Joseph to those men. They can take him to Egypt to work. Then we'll never see him again.'

They shouted to the men to stop. Then
they pulled Joseph up out of the well.

'What will you pay us for this strong
young man?' they asked.

Joseph's brothers sold him to the men for twenty silver coins and watched the camels go off to Egypt with Joseph walking behind.

They tore Joseph's coat and dipped it in the blood of an animal. The beautiful new coat looked horrible now.

When they went home they tried to look unhappy.

'Look what we've found,' they said to Jacob, holding up the coat. 'Do you think Joseph has been killed by a wild animal?'

Jacob took the coat and held it up.
'Joseph must be dead,' he said.

Jacob was so sad. He did not see that
his sons were glad to get rid of Joseph.

The brothers did not know that God
had important work for Joseph to do in
Egypt.

But first there were things Joseph
must learn.

Jacob was very sad. He thought that he would never see Joseph again. He did not know then that this was not the end of the story.

Joseph and the king of Egypt

This is the second part of the story of Joseph. In Egypt, far from his home and family, Joseph learned to trust God through the bad times. God took good care of Joseph: he had a special plan for him.

You will find the story in Genesis, chapters 39 to 47.

Joseph lived in a land called Egypt.
But his real home was in Canaan, where
his family lived. There he had a father
called Jacob, who loved him very much.
He also had eleven brothers.

Joseph found his new life very hard.
In Canaan he had been the son his
father, Jacob, loved most.

Here in Egypt people stared at him,
because he came from another country.
　'You can see he's not one of us,'
they said.

In Canaan he had been able to have everything he wanted, because his father was rich.

In Egypt he had been sold to a rich man. He was a slave. But he did his work so well that before long he had an important job. He had to look after the rich man's house.

God had not forgotten Joseph. But he wanted Joseph to change. He did not want him to be a spoiled boy who got his brothers into trouble.

He wanted Joseph to trust him and to become a man other people could trust.

One day Joseph was put in prison for something he had not done. Even in prison God helped him.

The prison was horrible. It was dark and smelly.

The jailer saw how hard Joseph worked. So he put him in charge of all the other prisoners.

Joseph made friends with the prisoners.
When two of them had puzzling dreams,
Joseph helped them.

'God will tell me what the dreams
mean,' he said, and he explained them.

'In three days' time you will be set free,' he said to one of the men. 'Please don't forget to ask someone to let me out too.'

This man's job was to bring wine to the king himself.

Sure enough, he was set free and worked for the king, just as Joseph had said.

But two years passed and Joseph was
still in prison. Then the king had a
dream, and the man remembered Joseph.

'I know someone who can explain
your dream,' he said to the king. 'His
God helps him.'

So the king sent for Joseph.

'I have had a very strange dream,'
he said. 'My servant says you can
explain it.'

'My God will help me,' said Joseph.

The king dreamed he was standing by
the great river of Egypt.

He saw seven fat cows come out of the
water and start to eat the grass.

Then he saw seven skinny cows come
out of the water. They ate up the
seven fat cows but stayed as thin
as before.

'I wish I knew what it meant,' he cried.

Joseph told the king, 'God wants you to know that there are going to be seven years when we will all have plenty of food to eat. But you must save some of the food, because for seven years after that there will not be enough.'

'I am glad God told us,' said the king.
'We must store up all the food we can.
    'We shall need someone in charge.
I think that you should do it.'

So Joseph became the most important man in Egypt. He stored up the food when there was plenty.

Then, when there was no harvest, the people came to buy food from him.

People came from other lands to buy
food too. Even in Canaan, where Joseph's
father lived, the harvests were poor
and the people were very hungry.

One day, when Joseph was busy in the
storehouse, he saw his own brothers
coming through the door. They did not
know this great man was Joseph.
And he did not tell them right away.
First he wanted to find out if they
were still as cruel.

When he knew they had really changed,
Joseph told them who he was. They were
very ashamed.

But Joseph said, 'Please don't be
sad. Look how God has cared for me.
Go and bring Jacob, my father. I want
you all to come and live with me in
Egypt. There are five more hungry years
to come.'

Jacob had been so sure that Joseph was dead. How glad he was to see him again!

He was happy to live in Egypt, where there was plenty of food.

Most of all, Jacob was glad that Joseph
was a man who could be trusted. God
had changed him, and he had changed
the cruel brothers.

Jacob thanked God for taking care
of Joseph in Egypt.

The princess and the baby

Jacob and his family came to Egypt to find
food. Joseph had saved them from starving.
They stayed on, the years passed, and the
family grew into a nation—people called
them the Israelites. Then trouble came...

You will find this story in Exodus (the
second book of the Bible), chapters 1 and 2.

There were many Israelites living in the
land of Egypt. It was not their own
country.

The Egyptians looked at the Israelites
who lived in their country and said,
'There are so many of them. They will
soon be taking over Egypt!'

There was a new king in Egypt. He looked at all the Israelites and said, 'Something must be done. There are too many of them. They might fight us and turn us out of our own land.'

'They are useful slaves, but we must think of a way to make them tired and weak so that they cannot fight as soldiers.'

So the king of Egypt made the
Israelites work very hard.

They had to start early in the
morning. They went back to their
homes when it was late at night.

The Israelites had to make bricks for the Egyptian cities. They had to do all the hard work on the farms too.

They became hot and tired. But they were still stronger than the Egyptians.

The Egyptians were afraid of them.

'I have a good idea,' said the king.
'We will kill all their baby boys when
they are born. Soon they will have no
young men to fight us.'

So the king of Egypt told the people, 'All the Israelite baby boys must be killed.'

The Israelites were very sad. They loved their baby boys. They wanted them to grow up to be strong young men.

One Israelite woman who had a baby
boy said to her little girl, Miriam,
'I can't let them kill him. I want to
watch him grow up. I love him so
much.'

So she made a tiny floating cradle for him and put it on the river among the reeds.

Every day they put him in his special hiding place. His sister Miriam sat on the river bank and watched.

One day Miriam saw the king's
daughter walking beside the river.
She had some servants with her.

Miriam did not know what to do. She
could not hide the cradle herself and
there was no time to get her mother.

'What's that?' asked the princess,
pointing to the tiny floating cradle.

They pulled the cradle to the river
bank, opened the lid and looked inside.
There was the little baby.

He was crying. But when he saw
the princess, he put out his hands to
touch her face.

'What a lovely baby,' said the princess.
'He is an Israelite. I wish I had
someone to look after him. Then I could
keep him.'

Then Miriam came down the bank to the path. 'I know someone who would look after him for you,' she said. 'I'll just go and get her.'

Miriam ran to get her mother. The princess did not know that she was the baby's own mother.

'Please look after him,' said the princess to the baby's mother. 'When he is old enough he can come and live at my palace. I shall call him Moses.'

Miriam and her mother were so happy
to have the baby boy back.

No one could kill him now, because
they knew that Moses belonged to the
princess.

Every day the little family watched
Moses grow. He learned to walk and
talk. He laughed and played with
Miriam by the river.

When Moses was old enough he went
to live at the palace with the princess.
He grew up as a rich young man.

He knew he was not an Egyptian. He often saw the Israelites as they worked at the palace. He saw how tired and sad they were.

'I wish I could help them,' he said.

God had not forgotten the Israelites. He knew they needed a strong leader to take them away from Egypt.

God wanted them to go back to the land of Canaan.

'I will give Moses the job of leading the Israelites out of Egypt,' said God. 'And I will be with him just as I was with Joseph.'

But that is another story.

Let my people go!

This story tells how Moses became the
leader of his people, the Israelites. It comes
from the book of Exodus, chapters 2 to 12.
God is in control of our world, as this story
shows—and he is a loving God. When his
people cry to him for help, he hears and
comes to their rescue.

Moses lived in the palace of the king of Egypt. He had everything he could wish for. But he was not an Egyptian — he was an Israelite.

The other Israelites were slaves. They had to work very hard, making bricks all day in the hot sun. If they stopped, they were whipped.

One day Moses saw an Egyptian being very cruel to an Israelite. He was so angry that he knocked the Egyptian down and killed him.

Moses was afraid of what the king
would do when he found out. So he ran
away from the city, to a place where no
one knew who he was. He worked as a
shepherd.

He often thought about the Israelites,
as he looked after the sheep.

One day, as Moses watched over his sheep, he saw a bush that was on fire.

'That's funny,' he said. 'The leaves are still green, even though it is burning.'

Then he heard a voice saying, 'Be
careful, Moses. This is a very special
place. I am the same God who spoke to
Abraham and Isaac and Jacob. I have
seen how my people are suffering. You
are going to lead them out of Egypt. Go
and speak to the king for me.'

Moses was afraid.

'The king will never listen to me,' he said. 'He will not even believe that you have spoken to me.'

But God told Moses to take his brother Aaron with him.

Moses and Aaron went to see the king.

'We have a message from our God,'
they said. 'Our God says "Let my people
go!"'

'I don't know your God,' said the king.
'I will not let you go.'

And he gave orders to his men to
make the Israelite slaves work even harder.

God told Moses and Aaron that he
would make the king let the Israelites go.

'If you don't let us go, the river will
turn to blood,' Moses said to the king.

The king would not listen. And the
river turned to blood.

'I will still not let the Israelites go,'
said the king.

God had promised Moses that he
would lead the Israelites out of Egypt to
their own land.

So Moses went to the king again and
said, 'Our God says "Let my people
go!"'

But the king would not listen. He was
angry.

The frogs that lived by the river did not like it now. They came up into the town. They jumped all over the rooms in the palace.

When the king saw all the frogs he said, 'Tell the Israelites they can go.'

But when the frogs had gone, he changed his mind.

After the frogs, there were gnats
everywhere, biting everyone.

'The Israelites can go!' shouted the
king.

But when the gnats had gone, he
changed his mind.

God then sent swarms of flies to the
land of Egypt. They were everywhere —
except where the Israelites lived.

The animals which belonged to the
Egyptians became sick. The Israelite
animals were well.

The king kept saying, 'Yes, you can go.'
But when the flies went away and the
animals were well, he changed his mind.
'You must stay here,' he said.

Moses and Aaron told the king, 'If you
don't let the Israelites go you will be
covered in boils and there will be
hailstorms too.'
The king did not care.

Soon the Egyptians had sore boils all
over them. Then there was a terrible
hailstorm. It beat down the plants and
hurt the people — except where the
Israelites lived.

'You can go away — now,' said the
king.

But when the boils went and the hail
stopped, the king changed his mind.

Moses told the king that God would send locusts to eat his grain. And that is what happened.

Then God said he would make the daytime as dark as night.

When these terrible things happened, the king wanted to get rid of the Israelites.

But as soon as they stopped, the king changed his mind.

Then God said to Moses, 'Tell the Israelites to get ready to go. Tell the king that tonight I am coming to Egypt. Because he has not obeyed me, the oldest child in each family will die.'

Moses told the Israelites to mark the doors of their own houses with blood from an animal. Then their oldest child would be safe.

It all happened as God said it would. All God's people were safe.

Then the king of Egypt asked Moses to take the Israelites away.

'God has given us so much trouble,' he said. 'He must want you very much.'

So God took the Israelites out of Egypt.
In the daytime he led them with a
special cloud. At night there was a
finger of fire, so that they could not lose
their way.

At last they were on their way to
Canaan, the land God had promised to
them.

Journey to the promised land

Moses has led the Israelites out of Egypt.
This is the story of how God brought them
to the new land of Canaan. You can find it
in Exodus chapters 20, 25 and 26, 32, and
Numbers chapter 13. The journey was long,
and there were hard lessons to learn.

The Israelites had lived in the land of Egypt for a long time. They had often wanted to live in a land of their own. But they were slaves and the king would not let them go.

God gave them a leader called Moses and he made the king say, 'Yes, you can go.' So Moses led the Israelites out of Egypt.

But the king of Egypt changed his mind. Suddenly the Israelites heard the sound of horses behind them. The Egyptians were chasing after them! They didn't know where to run.

In front of them was a wide sea of water. They looked at Moses in dismay.

'Don't be afraid,' Moses said. 'Watch and see what God will do.'

Then Moses held his stick out over the water. All night long a strong wind blew. It made a dry pathway. The Israelites hurried across.

But when the Egyptians tried to follow, the water came back and they could not cross. The Israelites were safe. They danced and sang for joy.

But before long God's people began to grumble. What was there to eat and drink in the desert?

'Trust me,' God said. And every morning he sent them special food. It lay on the ground like frost. It tasted like biscuits made with honey. The people called it manna.

When they cried out for meat, God sent
some birds called quails to eat.

When they complained that they were
thirsty, God told Moses to strike a big
rock with his stick. And water poured
out for them to drink.

God took great care of his people in
the desert.

Then God said to Moses, 'I need to talk to you about the way I want my people to live.'

The people were camped at the foot of Mount Sinai. So Moses went up the mountain to talk to God.

God gave Moses the laws he wanted the Israelites to keep. They are called the ten commandments.

Moses was gone long that the Israelites grew tired of waiting.

'What's the good of a God you can't see?' they said. So they melted down the gold from their jewelry and made it into a model of a calf.

'Let's pretend that this is God,' they said. They danced around the calf.

When Moses came back he was very angry. He smashed the calf into tiny pieces.

The people were very sorry for what they had done. They promised from now on to keep God's laws.

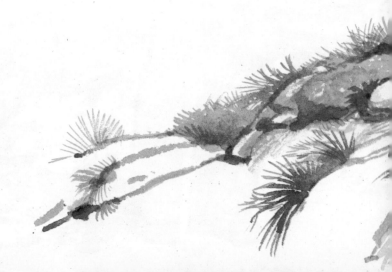

God had told Moses to make him a special tent. God's tent would be set up in the middle of the camp for everyone to see. Inside, it was very beautiful.

It had a special room where a copy of
God's laws was kept. The laws were
stored inside a box covered in gold, and
creatures made of gold covered the lid
with their wings.

Everywhere the Israelites went, they
would take God's tent and the special
box with them, to remind them of God.

One day, as they journeyed, God said to Moses, 'Across that river is Canaan, the land I am giving to you. Send some men over to look. Then they can tell you what it is like.'

So Moses sent twelve men to look at the
land. They brought back bunches of
grapes.

'It is a good land,' they said. 'But we
can't go in — there are giants to fight.'

But Joshua and Caleb, two of the men,
said, 'There's no need to be afraid if God
is with us.'

The Israelites would not listen to Joshua and Caleb.

'We're not going to fight giants,' they said. 'Let's choose a new leader and go back to Egypt.'

'When will you learn to trust me?' God asked them. 'I have taken care of you all this time. I have kept all my promises. And still you won't trust me! Now you will spend forty years more in the desert.'

Nothing would stop the people grumbling. Then one day there were snakes all around the tents. Many of the people were bitten by the snakes and died.

'It's because we didn't obey God,' the people said, and they begged God to forgive them.

God told Moses to put a metal snake onto a tall pole.

'God says that you must trust him,' Moses told them. 'If you have been bitten, look up at the metal snake and God will heal you.'

So the people obeyed God and they were healed.

The Israelites had not trusted God to
take them into the new land. Now Moses
was too old to be their leader.

God told Moses that Joshua was to be
the new leader.

So Moses took Joshua out in front of all
the Israelites.

'This is the man God has chosen to
take you into your new land,' he told
them.

The people were very sad when Moses died. He had been their leader for a long time.

Now that they had learned to trust God they were ready to follow Joshua into the new land of Canaan — the land promised to them by God.

The battle of
Jericho

The Israelites, under their new leader
Joshua, have crossed the wild lands from
Egypt. Now they are ready to move into the
land God has promised them. This exciting
story comes from Joshua, chapters 2 to 6.

The Israelites were camping by the River
Jordan. On the other side of the river
was the land of Canaan. God had
promised long ago that the Israelites
would live in this land.

They had spent many years in the
desert. At last the promised land was in
sight.

God said to Joshua, the leader, 'I promise to give you and your people the whole land of Canaan if you obey me.

'I shall be with you, just as I was with Moses,' God said, 'so there is no need to be afraid. I shall never leave you on your own.'

Joshua was glad that God had spoken to him. He knew they would have to fight the people who already lived in the land.

231

Joshua said to the Israelites, 'Come and get ready. We are going into the new land.'

The Israelites were very excited. They began to pack up their tents.

Joshua chose two men to spy out the land.

'We will get ready by the river here,' he said. 'You two must go over and find out about that big city called Jericho. We must fight our first battle there.'

233

The two men crossed the river to the new land of Canaan. They found the city of Jericho. It had high walls and strong gates. They met a woman called Rahab, who lived in a house in the city walls.

When the king of Jericho sent soldiers to catch the men, Rahab hid them under a pile of flax on the flat roof.

'I have heard of the wonderful things your God has done,' Rahab said. 'Please promise me that I will be safe when you fight against this city.'

The men promised, and after dark Rahab helped them to escape. Then they went back to Joshua.

The people were all ready to cross the river. There was no bridge, and they had no boats.

The men who carried the special box which held God's laws went first. It was covered in gold and it shone in the sun.

As they stepped into the river, the water stopped flowing. The men stood in the middle with the box. The people walked across the river on dry ground.

They were in Canaan at last! The
Israelites said 'Thank you' to God for
bringing them safely through the river.

Joshua told them to pick up twelve
large stones from the river.

They piled up the stones. Joshua said,
'Now everyone who comes past here will
point to these stones. They will
remember how God brought you into
this new land.'

Joshua and the Israelites walked towards Jericho. The city walls were high and the gates were locked. All the people were inside.

'I will give you this city,' said God. 'But it will take seven days to win the battle.

'Every day for six days you must walk once right around the city. Seven priests, blowing their trumpets, will walk in front of my special box. The soldiers who follow must keep quiet. On the seventh day you must walk around the city seven times. Then the people can shout, and the city will be yours.'

Joshua did just as God had told him. Each day they walked once around Jericho. All the people watched them from the city walls.

First came the men with the trumpets.
What a noise they made!

Then came the men with the special
box.

Then came the rest of the Israelites.
They were silent.

On the seventh day the Israelites walked around Jericho seven times.

The people in Jericho felt suddenly afraid. They could not understand what Joshua's army was doing.

Then, suddenly, Joshua told the Israelites to shout. They were really glad. They had been silent for so long.

And, when they shouted, the city walls of Jericho fell down!

The Israelites marched in and took the city, just as God had said.

'Go and keep your promise to rescue Rahab, because she helped you,' Joshua told them. 'Then we must destroy the city.'

The Israelites had won their first battle in the land God had promised to them.

Joshua knew that they must go on
trusting God.

'There will be many more battles to
fight,' he said, 'before the land will
belong to us. But God has promised that
he will always be with us.'

God speaks
to Samuel

The battle for Jericho was the first of many
battles to win the land God had promised
his people. Sometimes they were defeated,
and God gave them new champions to
come to their rescue—people like Deborah
and Gideon and Samson.

This next story comes from the time when
the Israelites were settled in the land. You
will find it in the first book of Samuel,
chapters 1 to 3. It tells of God's special plan
for one small boy.

Long ago, in the land of Israel, there was a priest called Eli. He served God in the temple. When he was a young man he loved God very much.

By the time he was an old man he had
two sons. They did not care about God.
They were cruel and greedy and the
Israelites were afraid of them.

The Israelites wanted a priest who
really loved God and would show them
the right way to live.

One of the Israelite women was called
Hannah. She was very sad, because she
had no children. She had often asked
God to give her a baby.

The worst times were when Hannah
and her husband met all their friends
for a feast at the temple in Shiloh.

'Haven't you had a baby yet?' they
would ask. Hannah just shook her head
and looked sad.

One time Hannah left the feast.
She was crying and she could not eat.
She went into God's house, where it was
quiet.

Eli, the old priest, was sitting in
his place by the door. But she did not

want to talk to Eli. She wanted to talk to God.

Hannah stood there, praying. Her lips moved but she made no sound.
    'Dear God, please give me a son,' she begged. 'I promise he will serve you all his life, here in your temple. You can see how unhappy I am.'

Eli came up to Hannah. He did not
know she was praying.

'What's the matter with you?' he said.
'Have you had too much wine at the
feast?'

'Oh no!' said Hannah, and she told him why she was talking to God.

'I'm sure God will hear you,' said Eli.

Hannah felt much better as she went back to the feast.

They went back home and very soon Hannah had some good news for her husband.

'God heard me,' she told him. 'I'm going to have a baby at last.'

When the baby was born, he was
beautiful. His hair was curly and his
hands were so tiny.

Hannah said he was the best baby
boy who had ever been born. They
called him Samuel.

Later on, Hannah had more children.

When Samuel was old enough, Hannah took him to the temple, just as she had promised. She missed him very much but she was glad she had someone so special to give to God.

She knew that Eli was very kind. She
wanted Samuel to grow up to love and
serve God.

Every year, when Hannah came to the
feast, she brought Samuel new clothes
she had made for him.

For a long time God had not been able
to talk to Eli. Eli was too busy
thinking about his wicked sons,
who did not care about God.

In those days only a few people
listened to what God had to say.

God wanted to talk to Samuel. He knew
that Samuel had never heard his voice.
   'I will speak to him at bedtime,
when it is quiet,' God said.

One night, Samuel was sleeping in the
temple.

'Samuel,' said a voice.

'Here I am,' replied Samuel, thinking
it was Eli. He went over to the old
priest. But Eli had not called him.
'Go back to bed,' said Eli.

Then Samuel heard the voice again.

He got up and went to Eli. But Eli
had not called him. So he went back
to bed.

'Samuel,' said the voice for the third
time.

Samuel got up and went to Eli once
again.

Then Eli said, 'God must be speaking
to you. Listen carefully to what he says.
Now go back to bed.'

When Samuel heard the voice again, he answered as Eli had told him. 'Speak, Lord, I am listening.'

God had a special message for him to give to Eli.

'Tell Eli that his sons have been very wicked,' God said. 'He has not made them stop, and I am going to punish them.'

Samuel did not want to make Eli sad,
but he knew he must give him the
message.

Eli knew that what God had said was
true.

After that Samuel often heard God
talking to him. Because he did as God
said, the people could trust him.
He showed them the right way to live.

David and Goliath

When he grew up, Samuel took Eli's place
as the priest of Israel. When the people
demanded a king, God told Samuel who to
choose. Saul was Israel's first king, but he
did not obey God, and that led to trouble.
So God sent Samuel to find a new king.

This story comes from the first book of
Samuel, chapter 17. It is one of the most
famous of all Bible stories.

David was the youngest of eight sons.
His father was a shepherd called Jesse.

When David was growing up, the
prophet Samuel visited Jesse's family. He
told them that, when King Saul died,
David would be the next king of Israel.

God had especially chosen him, so
David knew that God was with him in a
special way.

David worked hard.

'God has to teach me to be a really
good shepherd before he can make me a
good king,' he said.

David played the harp and sang his own
songs about God. King Saul sometimes
asked David to go to the palace and sing
for him. When the king was in a bad
mood, David's songs made him feel
better.

David's brothers were soldiers. They fought in King Saul's army. They were often away from home for a long time.

Their father was pleased that David was at home to keep him company. He was an old man and David helped him look after the sheep.

David often spent days and nights out
on the hills. He had to take the sheep to
places where there was grass and water.

There were lions, wild bears and
wolves living in the hills. David was
sometimes afraid.

He had to fight off the wild animals
to keep the lambs and sheep safe.

One day when David came back from
the hills, his father said, 'You can leave
the sheep for one of the men to look
after. I want you to go to visit your
brothers. Take them some good food and
bring me back news of them.'

So David packed some food and set off
on the journey.

It was a long way, but David knew
the hills very well.

At last he found his brothers with the Israelite army. They looked really frightened.

'What's the matter?' David asked.

They pointed to the hill across the valley. 'Over there, with the Philistine soldiers, is the giant Goliath,' they said. 'He wants one of us to fight him.'

'Well, why don't you?' asked David.
'You are the army of the living God. You will win.'

'If you're so brave, then come and tell the king you'll go,' sneered the brothers.

They were very surprised when David
did just as they said. He told the king
that he would go to fight Goliath, and
that God would fight for him.

'You must have my helmet and sword,'
said King Saul.

But everything was so heavy that
David could not stand up.

'I can't wear this,' David said, 'I'll just
take the sling and stones I use when I
am a shepherd.'

He took his sling and carefully chose
five smooth stones from beside the
stream.

285

When Goliath saw David walking across the valley towards him, he laughed so loudly that the Israelites had to cover up their ears.

Goliath had a sword and a shield.

But when he saw that David had brought only stones and a sling, he was angry.

'Do you think you are only fighting to keep your sheep safe?' he jeered.

But David knew how to fight with
stones. He took out his sling as he
walked. He fitted a stone into it.

When he was close to Goliath he
shouted, 'I come against you in the
name of the living God!'

David swung the sling around and around above his head. When he let go, the stone flew out and hit Goliath on his forehead. It was just the one place where he could be hurt.

The stone killed Goliath.

David drew the giant's own sword and cut off his head.

When the Philistines saw that Goliath was dead, they ran away.

The Israelites cheered when they saw what David had done to Goliath. They ran after the Philistines, driving them out of their land.

All the Israelites heard that David had won the battle. They knew the Philistines had run away.

They danced in the streets and sang songs about David, the brave shepherd.

King Saul grew jealous because everyone was talking about David.

David had learned to trust God when he was a shepherd. Now he had killed a giant because he knew that the God of Israel was the living God, who helps his people.

David would know how to trust God when he became king.

King David

David was a shepherd boy when God chose
him to be the king of Israel. This story is
about some of his adventures before he
became king.

You can find them in the first book of
Samuel, beginning at chapter 18.

Everybody at King Saul's palace knew about David the shepherd boy. He had killed the giant Goliath. And he played beautiful music on his harp.

After the battle with Goliath David went
to live at King Saul's palace. There he
met Jonathan, the king's son. They liked
one another at once. They were best
friends and shared all their secrets.

297

David was famous. All the Israelites
liked him. He was so brave.

The king became very jealous.

'They will be making him king next!'
he thought to himself. 'I must get rid of
him. Even Jonathan loves him best.'

One day David was playing some music for the king, to cheer him up. Suddenly King Saul picked up a spear and threw it at David.

David jumped out of the way. The spear stuck quivering in the wall. David ran away from the palace.

Jonathan was very sad when David went away.

'Everybody loves David,' Jonathan told King Saul. 'We can all see that he is growing up to be a great man.'

But that just made the king hate David more. Jonathan told David that Saul was trying to kill him.

David knew that God would take care of him. He had promised that one day David would be king of Israel.

But still Saul tried to get rid of David.

One night there was a great feast in the palace.

'How can I come to the feast if the king wants to kill me?' David said to Jonathan. 'If he asks where I am, tell him I have gone to see my family.'

Jonathan promised to tell the king.

At the great feast that night King Saul asked where David was. When Jonathan told him, he went into a rage.

'Why are you taking sides with David?' he said. 'You are my son. You should be king when I die. If I don't kill David, he will become king.'

Jonathan went to tell David.

'You must never come back while my father is alive. He will kill you.'

David did not know where to run but he knew God would show him.

He went to live up in the hills where
there were some caves. Some of his
friends went with him.

David knew that he was in danger,
but he was sure that God would look
after him.

The king kept trying to find David, to kill him. One day King Saul sat down to rest, just outside the cave where David was hiding. David crept out and cut a piece off the king's robe.

As the king walked away, David called
out to him, 'Why are you trying to kill
me? I came very close to you just now,
but I did not hurt you.'

The king saw that David was holding
a piece of his robe and he knew that
David was right.

But before long the king forgot that
David had not hurt him on the hillside.
He went hunting for David again.

This time David crept into the king's camp at night. He took the spear that was stuck in the ground at King Saul's head.

In the morning he called out, 'King Saul, where is your spear?'

It was gone. Saul knew that once again David could have killed him. So Saul went away.

One day David heard news of a terrible
battle. King Saul and Jonathan had been
killed by the Philistines.

It was the saddest day of David's life.
He missed his best friend very much.

The Israelites crowned David king. God's
promise had come true. There were still
many battles to fight. But they knew
that God would help David to be a good
leader.

David captured the city of Jerusalem.
There was great celebration when he
brought the special box which held
God's laws into the city. David himself
danced for joy.

David wanted to build a temple for
God in Jerusalem. He made all the plans.
But there were still many battles to fight.

David and his army fought all the
enemies of the Israelites and at last
there was peace.

313

King David ruled over a great nation.
He loved God all his life. He did not
always obey God. But when he had
done wrong he was sorry and always
asked God to forgive him.

God kept all the promises he had made
to King David.

'Your son, Solomon, will be king after
you,' God said. 'He is the one who will
build that temple for me.'

Solomon's golden temple

God did not let King David build him a
temple in Jerusalem, but he made David a
special promise. The line of kings that
David began would never die out. When
David's son Solomon became king, God's
promise and David's dream of a temple
began to come true.

This story comes from the first book of
Kings, chapters 3 to 10.

'Long live King Solomon!' shouted all the
people.

Solomon was the new king of Israel.
He wanted to be a good king like his
father, David.

Solomon knew that when his father
had obeyed God everything went well.
So he made up his mind that he would
be the kind of king who obeyed God,
too.

God was pleased that Solomon had decided to obey him. He spoke to Solomon in a dream.

'What would you like from me as a special present?' God said. 'You can have whatever you ask for.'

'What I really need,' said Solomon, 'is wisdom. I don't see how I can make a good job of being king unless you make me wise.'

God was pleased with Solomon's answer.

'I will give you wisdom,' he said, 'and fame and riches, too.'

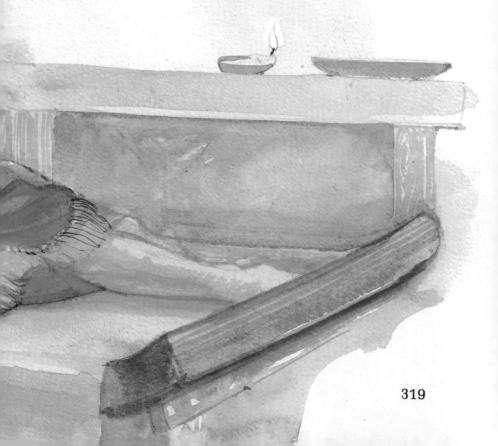

God made Solomon very wise. All the
Israelites came with their problems to
the king, because he had good answers.

Even people from other lands came.
They heard that God had made Solomon
very rich and very wise.

One day the queen of Sheba came on a long journey to visit Solomon.

She asked him questions. She listened to his answers.

She looked at his beautiful palace and all his riches.

'They told me how rich you are,' she said to Solomon. 'They told me you are very wise. I thought I would be disappointed when I saw what you were really like. But now I know that you are twice as magnificent as they told me.'

Solomon looked around his land.

When the Israelites had first come to the land they had lived in tents.

Now they had houses to live in, and
strong walled cities.

But there was no house for God.

'We ought to build God a beautiful
house,' said Solomon, 'the temple my
father, King David, planned.

'It will be the most beautiful temple
ever built. And inside it we will keep the
special box which holds God's laws,
to remind us of his promises.'

So Solomon set to work.

'We will make it from stone, wood and gold,' said Solomon. 'And we will use the very best workmen.'

Solomon sent a message to the king of
Tyre.

'I'm building a temple for God,' he
said. 'Please send me some of your
beautiful cedar trees, so that the temple
can be really special.'

Solomon sent for the men who were
good at working in stone and wood and
gold.

'This is going to be a special building
for God,' he said. 'We must not have a
lot of noise and shouting while it is
being made. Do all the work here in the
quarry. Then carry the stones to the
temple and put them together.'

They all worked hard for a very long
time. The house of God was not big, like
a cathedral, but it was very beautiful.
And there was room all around it for the
people to come.

At last it was finished. They could bring the special box into the new temple.

It had its own room. The walls were covered in gold.

When Solomon and the people saw the finished temple, they knew it was very beautiful.

It was the very best they could build.

Solomon called the people together.

'The temple is finished,' he said. 'The special box is inside. We must thank God for helping us to build the temple.'

So Solomon and the people prayed.

'We know that you are far too great to live in one place on earth,' they said. 'But please make the temple a very special place where we know you are near us.'

Suddenly a bright, dazzling light filled the temple. They knew that God had heard their prayer.

God had given his people a great and
wise king.

As they went to worship God at his
beautiful temple, they knew that the city
of Jerusalem was now a very special
place. God himself was there with them.

Elijah and the prophets of Baal

King Solomon was a great and wise king, but after he died his kingdom split in two— Israel in the north and Judah in the south. The kings of Israel did not obey God, and there was trouble. But God still loved his people. He sent special messengers, the prophets, to warn and encourage them. Elijah was one of the most famous prophets.

You can find this story in the first book of Kings, chapter 18.

There had been no rain in Israel for two
years. And it was all King Ahab's fault.

God had sent the prophet Elijah to tell
the king, 'God is angry because you
have disobeyed him and you worship
false gods. When you start to obey him,
he will send rain.'

King Ahab had taken no notice.
Now God told Elijah he must go to
see the king again.

Elijah walked through the land of Israel. Everywhere was brown and dry. The animals in the fields were thin, because there was no grass. The people he passed looked tired and thin, too. There were no plants on their farms, so they had nothing to eat.

When the people saw Elijah coming, they said, 'You must be very brave. The king is angry. He has been looking for you everywhere.'

When King Ahab saw Elijah coming, he
shouted: 'Here comes the trouble-maker!'
    Elijah said, 'I'm not the trouble-maker.
You are. If you had obeyed God none of
this would have happened.'

'You know that you must worship God,'
Elijah said. 'Your Baal is a false god. He
has no power. Tell the prophets of Baal
and the people to meet me on Mount
Carmel, and then we shall see which is
the real God.'

So King Ahab told the prophets of Baal and all the Israelites to go to Mount Carmel.

Elijah said, 'Let us both offer a bull as a sacrifice. Then you pray to Baal; I shall pray to God. The God who sends fire is the true God.'

When they all reached the top of the
mountain, the prophets of Baal built an
altar of stones.

They put their sacrifice on the altar
but they did not light the fire.

Then Elijah stood up and shouted, so
that all the people could hear him.

'It's time you made up your minds.
There can only be one living God. Stop
trying to serve both Baal and the God of
Israel.

'Let us see which God is powerful enough to send fire. Then we will know which is the living God who answers prayer, Baal or the God of Israel.'

Elijah told the prophets of Baal to have
their turn first. They prayed and
shouted to Baal for most of the day.

They clapped their hands and danced around the altar, but no fire came.

Elijah started to tease them.

'Baal must be asleep,' he said. 'Shout louder and wake him up. Then perhaps he'll send you fire.'

They started to scream to Baal. They danced faster and faster. But still no fire came.

353

Now it was Elijah's turn.

He called all the Israelites to come closer, so that they could see what was happening. He piled up stones to make an altar and put his sacrifice on it.

He dug a trench all around the altar.

Then he poured water all over the altar, until everything was soaking wet. The water ran down and filled the trench.

355

Then Elijah stood in front of the altar. He prayed so that everyone could hear him.

'Lord God, please prove to your people that you are the God of Israel. I want them to know that you are the only living God.'

Suddenly there was fire on Elijah's altar. It blazed hot and red, and the smoke swirled into the air. It burned up everything. It even made the water boil away.

The people shouted: 'The God of Israel is the God who hears us. We will serve the living God.'

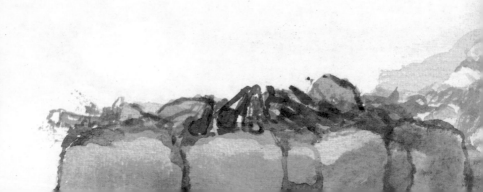

357

'You can go home now,' Elijah told the king. 'I can hear the rain coming.'

Away across the sea was a small, dark cloud. It came quickly. Soon the sky darkened and big drops of rain began to fall. God's people had come back to him. The grass would grow again. The thirsty days were over.

Jeremiah and the great disaster

The northern kingdom of Israel took no notice of God's warnings—and in the end the kingdom was conquered by the Assyrians. In the south, the kingdom of Judah was in great danger. Only their good kings saved them. But by Jeremiah's time the people of Judah, too, were refusing to trust God and listen to his prophets.

The story of Jeremiah is told in the book called by his name.

Jeremiah was a young man when God first spoke to him. He was very surprised. It had never happened to him before. It was really quite astonishing.

God said, 'I chose you even before you were born, to be a prophet and speak to my people for me. Now it's time for you to begin.'

Jeremiah was very shy.

'I can't possibly be a prophet,' he said, 'I'm too young, and anyway I wouldn't know what to say.'

'Do you think that I will leave you to do the job on your own?' asked God. 'Of course not! I shall give you the words to speak.' And Jeremiah felt a finger touch his lips.

God told Jeremiah how much he loved
his people. He had loved them from the
very beginning, when he chose Abraham
to start a new nation.

'The trouble is,' God said, 'they so often forget me. They say that they love me and then they go off and worship idols — gods made of stone and wood. Now you are going to be my prophet. You must tell my people to change their ways. Before it is too late.'

So Jeremiah went out to start his new job. God told him to go to the temple in Jerusalem. If Jeremiah preached there, everyone would hear him.

'God says you must change the way you live,' he told the people. 'God says you do all the things he hates. Then you come to this temple, which is his special place. You have no right to come here unless you change.'

The people listened, but they did not do what God told them to do.

Jeremiah reminded the people of the special promises God had given to Abraham.

'God promised to protect the whole nation if you served him,' he told them.

'You have broken your part of the promise,' Jeremiah said sadly. 'God still loves you, but he can't keep his part of the promise unless you change the way you live.'

The people listened, but still they did not change — as God had told them to do.

So Jeremiah pointed to the potter's workshop, near the temple.

'See the potter?' he asked them. 'If the pot he is making goes the wrong shape, what does he do?'

The people said, 'He squashes it flat and starts again. Everyone knows that.'

'Yes, and that is what God will do, if the nation he is making goes wrong,' said Jeremiah.

The people listened quietly.

371

God told Jeremiah to buy a large clay jar. Then Jeremiah said to the people, 'God says that because you have disobeyed him he will punish you.'

He lifted the clay jar above his head and then smashed it on the ground.

'This is what God will do to his people,' he said. 'The king of Babylon will come and destroy this city.'

The people looked at the thousands of pieces. Nobody would ever be able to mend it.

The crowd grew angry.

'What right has Jeremiah to pretend to be a prophet?' they said. 'Someone must stop him.'

They did not like being told that they were wrong.

But, although he was frightened,
Jeremiah would not stop speaking. He
spoke in the temple. He sent messages to
the king. In the end, the king sent
guards to arrest him.

The king's men took Jeremiah and threw
him into a dry well in the palace
courtyard. It was deep and slippery. He
wouldn't be able to talk to anyone there!

But Jeremiah had a friend in the city.
He went to the king and said, 'Your
Majesty, it was wrong to throw Jeremiah
down the well. Our enemies have
surrounded the city. There is no food.
Jeremiah will starve and die. Please let
me rescue him.'

So Jeremiah was pulled up out of the
well with a rope and kept in prison
instead.

But God meant what he had said. He
was going to punish his people.

One day the enemy broke into the city. They tied up the Israelites with ropes and took them away as slaves to Babylon.

They smashed the houses and burned the palace. God's temple was now just a heap of stones. Only a few people were left in the city — and one of them was Jeremiah.

Jeremiah was very sad, hungry and
lonely. He looked around the city which
had once been so beautiful. Now it was
ugly and empty.

Then he remembered something God had told him.

'The city of Jerusalem will be spoiled and the people taken prisoner. But, when my people have learned to obey me, I promise that I will bring them back home to Jerusalem.'

God still loved his people. There was hope.

Daniel in the lions' den

King Nebuchadnezzar of Babylon took
prisoners from Judah. Daniel was one of
them. He was taken from his home and his
family, and made to live far away in a
foreign land. But he never stopped loving
God and obeying him.

This very famous story comes from the
book of Daniel.

Daniel lived in Babylon. He was not in
his own country. Daniel was a prisoner.
But because he was clever he was
chosen for work in the king's palace.

Daniel longed to be back home in
Jerusalem. He prayed to God three
times a day in his little room.

One day Babylon was captured by the
Persians. There was a new king, called
Darius. He knew that Daniel was a very
wise man, even though he was a foreign
prisoner.

Whenever he needed help and advice
the king sent for Daniel. Daniel always
asked God for the right answers.

There were many other wise men in
Babylon. They were jealous of Daniel.
  'Why doesn't the king call for us
when he needs help,' they said, 'instead
of that foreigner, Daniel?'

The wise men held a secret meeting.

'Something will have to be done about Daniel,' they said. 'How can we get rid of him?'

'The trouble is,' one of them grumbled, 'he's such a good man. We can't get him into trouble for anything, unless it's to do with his God.'

The next day they went to speak to the king.

'King Darius, live for ever,' they said. 'You are the best king Babylon has ever had. Nothing is too difficult for you to do.'

The king felt most important as he listened to them.

'Why don't you make a law,' the men
went on, 'to say that for the next thirty
days the people must ask no one but
you for whatever they need. Then they'll
know how great you are.'

'What a good idea!' said the king.

Daniel was in the palace when the new law was read out. It said that anyone who disobeyed the law and asked his god for anything would be thrown into the pit where the lions were kept.

The men followed Daniel home. Then they hid where they could watch him.

'Let's hope he asks his God for something,' they whispered. 'Then we'll be rid of him.'

Daniel thought about the new law as he went home.

He always thanked God for his help and for taking care of him.

But there were things he asked for, too.

The king's law had said he must not do
that.

Daniel went to the open window. He
started to pray out loud to God, just as
he always had.

The men who were hiding nearby saw
Daniel at the window. They heard him
asking his God for what he needed.

They were so pleased. They ran to tell
the king that Daniel had broken his law.

The king was very sad. He did not want
to hurt Daniel.

'I wish I hadn't made that new law,'
said the king. 'Those men are only
jealous. Now I shall have to throw
Daniel to the lions.'

King Darius could not break his own
law. He had written his own name on
the paper when the law was made. The
law could not be changed.

So the soldiers from the palace went to get Daniel.

They took him to the place where the lions were kept and threw him in.

The king went back to his palace. He knew how silly he had been to make a law like that.

He could not sleep.

'I do hope Daniel's God is as powerful as Daniel says he is,' the king thought. 'Perhaps he will save Daniel from the lions.'

Early the next morning, before the palace servants were awake, King Darius got up. Everywhere was silent. He hurried to the lion-pit.

'Daniel, can you hear me?' the king called out. 'Has your God been able to save you from the sharp teeth of the lions?' He did not expect an answer.

'Yes, he has,' shouted back Daniel. 'They haven't opened their mouths all night. God knew I had done no wrong. I am perfectly all right.'

Quickly the king ordered his servants to pull Daniel up out of the lion-pit.

He punished the men who had been so jealous. He wrote to all the people in his great empire.

'I command you to respect Daniel's God. He is a living God and he will rule for ever. He saved Daniel from the lions.'

Queen Esther
saves her people

Esther was a Jewish girl who became queen
in the far-off land of Persia. Her family had
been taken from Judah when the king of
Babylon captured Jerusalem. But God still
loves and cares for his people, wherever
they are—as this story shows. It comes
from the book of Esther.

One day, in the city of Susa, there was
great excitement. The king of Persia was
going to choose a new queen.

The most beautiful girls in the land
were sent to the palace. For a whole
year they were given special food. They
were made even more beautiful, ready
for King Xerxes to choose the one he
liked best.

One of the girls sent to the palace was called Esther. She was Jewish. Her parents had died when she was a little girl, so she lived with her cousin, Mordecai.

'You are so beautiful, I'm sure the king will choose you,' said Mordecai. 'But don't tell him you are Jewish. Keep that a secret.'

Esther did as Mordecai told her. She
kept her secret. King Xerxes chose her
out of all the other girls, because she
was so lovely.

The whole city had a holiday. The
king gave everyone presents to celebrate
his new queen, Esther.

Esther enjoyed living at the palace. Her cousin, Mordecai, worked there. He told Esther what was happening in other parts of the busy palace.

One day he was very worried.

'I have just heard two men planning to kill the king,' he said.

Immediately Esther told the king. When he found out that the story was true, he punished the two men.

The king told his servant to write down Mordecai's name in his diary, so that he would not forget the man who had saved his life.

A few years later, King Xerxes had a
new Prime Minister. His name was
Haman, and he was proud and wicked.
  When Haman walked in the palace
gardens and in the city square, he made
everyone bow down to him.

But Mordecai did not bow down to
Haman.

'I bow down only to the living God,'
he told the people. 'I cannot bow down
to Haman.' So Haman hated him.

Haman decided it was time to get rid of
Mordecai and all his people. He went to
the king.

'Scattered across your land,' he told
the king, 'are people who do not live like
us. They do not obey the laws of the
land, and as I am your Prime Minister
I advise you to get rid of them.'

Haman was a clever man. When he spoke like that, King Xerxes thought the idea was very sensible. He gave the order that on a certain day all the Jews should be killed.

When Mordecai heard of the king's order, he was very upset. Mordecai went to see Esther.

'This is all Haman's fault,' said Mordecai. 'He wouldn't dare to do it if he knew that you were a Jewish girl, too. You must go and ask the king to save our lives.'

'I am only allowed to go to the king if he asks for me,' said Queen Esther. 'He may kill me if I go without an invitation. You must ask all our people to pray for me.'

'Of course we will pray for you,' said Mordecai. 'Perhaps this is why God made you queen of Persia: so that you could save our people.'

Esther went quietly to the king's room. She knew she was breaking the palace rules. She was so thankful when he looked pleased to see her.

'What would you like, Esther?' said the king.

'Please come to a special banquet I am having,' said Queen Esther. 'I would like you to bring Haman with you.'

The king and Haman came to the
banquet. It was a delicious meal. Haman
felt very proud of being at the queen's
banquet.

That night King Xerxes could not get to sleep. He tossed and turned, grunted and yawned, but still he was wide awake. In the end he started to read his diary.

He read about the two men who had plotted to kill him.

'Have I ever rewarded Mordecai?' he asked his servant.

'No, never,' the servant said.

The next day King Xerxes gave
Mordecai some gorgeous robes and put
him on his own horse. He told Haman to
go ahead of the horse around the city
square, shouting, 'Look how the king
rewards a man who serves him well.'
Haman just hated doing that.

The next night the king and Haman
went to see the queen again.

'I want to give you a present,' the king
said to Esther. 'You can have anything
you like. What can I give you?'

Esther was trembling with fear. She
knew she must tell the king now about
the plot to kill the Jews.

'There is only one present I really want,'
Esther said. 'I am a Jew. I want you to
change the order which says all the Jews
must be killed.'

'Who told me to make such a terrible
order?' asked the king.

'That man did,' said Queen Esther,
and pointed at Haman.

The king looked at Haman. Haman was trying to run away. The servants in the palace caught him.

'He wanted to kill my queen and Mordecai and all the Jews!' shouted the king. 'Get rid of him instead.'

So Mordecai was made Prime Minister in place of Haman.

The advice he gave the king was always wise and good. God's people were safe, living in the land of Persia.

Esther was given all the riches which had belonged to Haman.

She was so glad she had trusted the living God to keep her safe when she was frightened. And she thanked God every day, because he had saved his people.

Nehemiah's greatest day

God's people had disobeyed him. They had
been taken to far-off Babylon as prisoners.
Then a new king, Cyrus the Persian, came
to the throne and some of them went home
to Jerusalem to build God's temple again.
But the city walls were broken down. This is
what happened when Nehemiah heard
about it...

The story comes from the book of
Nehemiah.

Nehemiah was an exile. Years before, his
family and many others had been taken
prisoner by the king of Babylon and
marched away from home to work in a
far-off land. When the king of Persia
conquered Babylon, some of the people
went back home. But Nehemiah was left
behind.

Nehemiah worked in the king's palace at Susa. It was his job to serve the king's wine. He was an important man.

Nehemiah often felt very homesick. He remembered the beautiful city of Jerusalem before it was destroyed. How happy his people had been when they lived there together.

One day, Nehemiah's brother and some other men visited him at the palace.

'What is happening at home?' Nehemiah asked. 'Are the people who have gone back building Jerusalem again?'

The men had nothing but bad news for Nehemiah.

'No,' they said. 'The city of Jerusalem is still just a pile of stones. The walls and gates are all broken down.'

So Nehemiah prayed to God.

'You have kept all the promises you made to your people,' Nehemiah said to God.

'We are the ones who have done wrong,' he said sadly. 'That's why we are prisoners here. But please hear my prayer and keep your promise to take us back home.'

When Nehemiah had prayed he went on
with his work. He took the wine to the
table where the king was waiting.

The king looked at Nehemiah.

'You seem very sad,' he said. 'What is
the matter?'

Nehemiah thought he would be punished
for looking sad.

'I am really sorry,' he said, 'but I just
cannot help it. Someone has told me that
Jerusalem is still a pile of stones and
nobody seems to care.'

'What do you want me to do?' asked the
king.

'Please let me go back to rebuild the
city of Jerusalem,' Nehemiah said.

The king said he would let Nehemiah go.
They talked for a long time about how
long it would take and what Nehemiah
would need for the job.

'God really answered my prayer,'
thought Nehemiah, as he went to bed
that night.

It was a long, dangerous journey for
Nehemiah and his men. When at last
they saw Jerusalem they were sad.

That night, when it was dark,
Nehemiah rode on a donkey right
around the city with a few friends.

'What a lot of work there is to do,'
they whispered to each other.

The next day Nehemiah spoke to all the
people.

'God has given us this job to do,' said
Nehemiah. 'He will help us to do it well.'

So they divided into groups. Each
group worked on the section of the city
wall which was near their own homes.

The enemies of God's people saw them building Jerusalem again. They started to tease them.

'What do you think you are doing?' they said. 'You'll never build a wall strong enough even to keep a fox out!'

But when they saw the walls growing strong and high they grew really angry.

They tried to think of plans to break down the walls again.

Nehemiah and his men had to watch out for attack all the time. So some of the men built the wall while others stood on guard. Even the builders wore swords.

441

When the city wall and the gates were finished Nehemiah called all the Jews who still lived nearby to come to the city.

He asked Ezra the priest to read to all the people God's special message to them.

When the Israelites heard what God was saying to them they felt full of praise for their wonderful God. They felt sad, too, that they had not always obeyed him.

'At last,' said Nehemiah, 'the city is strong. We can worship God in his temple and ask him to make it special again.'

So all the Israelites went up the steps to
the top of the city walls.

They blew trumpets and sang at the
tops of their voices as they walked
around the city. Everyone outside could
hear them praising God.

God had warned his people that if they disobeyed him they would have to leave their homes — and they did. But he had made them a promise, too.

God had said that if they loved him and turned to him for help he would bring them back to Jerusalem. Now they were home again — home in Jerusalem.

As they marched around their new-built city God's people thanked him for keeping his promise.

All the stories in Part 1 of *The Lion Story Bible* come from the Old Testament. There are many more, which you can read for yourself. But God's story did not end with Nehemiah. God was planning to rescue people from all the trouble their disobedience had caused. Abraham and the nation he founded were part of God's plan. But there was more to come.

Part 2 of *The Lion Story Bible* brings together twenty stories from the New Testament. They tell of one very special person—Jesus Christ—who was sent by God to save all people everywhere.